allotment &
vegetable garden
planner

CICO BOOKS
LONDON NEW YORK

Contents

Getting started

This specially designed journal is an indispensable companion for gardeners, packed with record pages to keep track of your planting plans, so you know which varieties grew well, when you planted seeds, which crops were rotated, germination times, and more. This chapter looks at all the elements you need to get the most out of your garden.

Also included are pages for keeping notes, space for jotting down favorite websites and stores, as well as grids to plan your plot and year planners to help you schedule what you need to do when. All of these pages are aimed to make the day you are presented with your first patch of ground for cultivating organic produce less daunting and more exhilarating. The earth is packed with potential, ready to be unlocked with some seeds, a few tools, patience, and perseverance. Along with the health and ecological benefits of growing your own food, there is the sheer therapeutic value to be derived from gardening and from eating the fruits of one's labor. In order to get great results from your plot you'll need to put in some hard work and preparation. After you have cleared the ground of weeds and any unwanted plants, preparing the soil properly will pay dividends at harvest time. It's also important to plan what will grow where as some crops are site specific.

planning your plot

Take some time to consider the layout of your plot before you start planting. Consider factors like how much space each plant will take up, crop rotation, companion planting, the direction of sunlight, and location of water. Use the grids provided to work out how you want your garden to be. A careful hour spent deciding what to plant where will save a lot of time and effort later in the growing process.

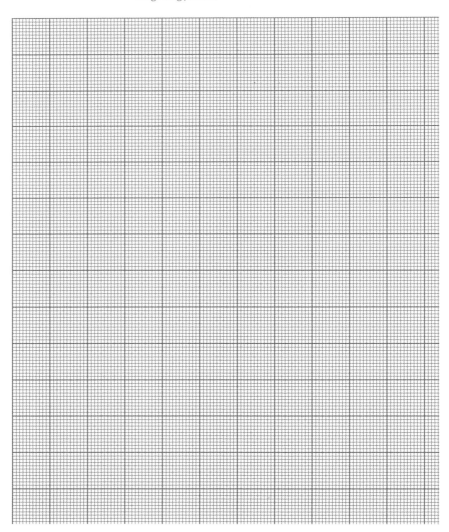

what to grow

Depending on where you live, there are hundreds of different vegetables, fruits, and herbs in just as many varieties. Try experimenting—you will soon find out what suits your soil, your climate, and your patience. To avoid gluts of the same foods, sow as wide a variety as possible, and try to plant crops that can be harvested at different times of the year. It is also wise to choose those vegetables and fruits that are expensive to buy, as well as the ones that you are particularly fond of.

The following can be grown successfully in the vegetable garden or allotment:

Vegetables

artichokes	eggplants (aubergine)	pole lima beans
asparagus	fava (broad) beans	potatoes
beets	fennel	pumpkins
bell peppers	garlic	radishes
borlotti beans	green beans	rutabagas (swede)
broccoli	green (spring) onions	scarlet-runner beans
Brussels sprouts	Jerusalem artichokes	shallots
cabbages	kale	sprouting broccoli
carrots	kohlrabi	squash
cauliflower	leeks	sweet potatoes
celeriac	lettuce	tomatoes
celery	marrows	turnips
corn	onions	zucchini (courgettes)
cucumbers	parsnips	
	peas	

Fruit
blueberries
gooseberries
grapes
raspberries
red currants
rhubarb
strawberries
white currants

Herbs
basil
cilantro (coriander)
mint
oregano
parsley
rosemary
sage
tarragon
thyme

getting started

tools and equipment

Gardeners need only a few small basic tools to get started, none of which need much storage space. Here's a list of the essentials, so gather them up and allocate them a spot where they can be kept together.

Large tools

When buying any tool, always try a pick an item where the head is made of forged steel. as they are less likely to bend or snap than other metals or plastics. Larger tools come in a variety of shapes, weights, materials, and sizes, so pick one that feels comfortable to use.

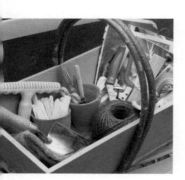

Keep your hand tools in good condition by storing them neatly in a basket or trug and by cleaning on a regular basis.

If you are planning on digging up or loosening ground, a spade is essential. Check the head is made from a material that won't rust easily and that the tread is large enough to get a good foothold on. A fork is often used to break up soil and to lift up plants. The tines, or prongs, can vary in width, with wider gaps more useful for larger crops such as potatoes. A rake is used to level the soil, but can also be used for weeding and clearing unwanted loose materials.

Hand tools

A good hand trowel is essential. Make sure it is strong and the joints are properly welded as cheaper tools may bend and become misshapen. Also, check the handle is securely fixed to the metal part of the trowel. Grip it to make sure it's ergonomically suited to your hand and comfortable to use. Some people also like a small fork for surface weeding.

Pruning shears (secateurs)

When planting up, you may need to cut away dead wood, leaves or flowers, or even plant labels. Invest in a good-quality pair of pruning shears (secateurs) that are sharp enough to make clean cuts, even in woody stems, and thereby promote healthy regrowth. The best for delicate stems are the "bypass" type, which have double blades like a pair of scissors. "Anvil" type shears have a blade on one side and

getting started

flat surface to cut against on the other. Some people find these useful when cutting woody stems, but even then, they are unlikely to produce the clean cut of bypass. Again, try before you buy, checking the grip suits your hand.

Although they are more expensive, these tools with their forged steel heads are a worthwhile investment as they will last a lot longer than some of the cheaper versions available in stores.

Watering can or hose

Plants need to be watered regularly to aid growth and stop them drying out. As you will be starting off with using young plants, ensure your watering can or hose has a fine rose attachment so that there is no damage to delicate petals or foliage.

Gardening gloves

Not necessary, but nice! Gardening gloves provide excellent protection against thorns and help keep your hands clean. Look for some that are not too bulky and fit your hands well. Disposable latex gloves from the pharmacy can be useful, too, keeping your hands clean while you work.

getting started

soil

Understanding the type of soil an allotment or vegetable garden consists of is vital when deciding which crops to grow. Soil is generally made up of at least one of three materials: clay, silt, and sand. The perfect soil will have a bit of all three, but don't worry if your plot is predominately one type, as all the types will have their own advantages and disadvantages

Potatoes flourish in loose soil that drains quickly.

Clay soil

Soils of a clay composition are notoriously hard to work with as they have a small particle size that retains water and a sticky, malleable structure. When it rains clay soils do not drain quickly, which can damage the roots of plants, and when the weather is hot the soil bakes solid and cracks, making it hard to work with. However, clay soils are full of nutrients and with some careful cultivation will yield a good crop, particularly if growing brassicas such as kale, broccoli, or cabbage.

Silt soil

Silt soils are similar in characteristics to clay, but feel less firm and slightly slippery to the touch. They retain water and nutrients, but consist of medium-sized particles, which means they are less likely to become waterlogged. Allotments and gardens near rivers will often compromise of silt soil as it is easily transported in water and deposited when a river floods. Most plants will grow in silt, just make sure water can drain away and the soil does not come too compacted.

Check the information on seed packets before you begin planting to see if the plant will be suited to the type of soil you have.

Sandy soil

Sandy soils are easier than clay soils to work with as they are lighter, with a gritty, crumbly texture, and easier to cultivate. However, due to a larger particle size water and nutrients can drain away quickly, making them less fertile and in need of regular monitoring to avoid drying out. In the spring months sandy soils heat up quickly, which will encourage the growth of new seedlings. With regular watering most vegetables will do well in sandy soil, including potatoes, peppers, parsnips, and carrots. Fruits, such as raspberries, peaches, plums, strawberries, and tomatoes, and herbs including sage, rosemary, and oregano will also do well.

getting started

15

preparing your plot

Once you have worked out what you plan to plant in your kitchen garden or allotment, the next step is to start preparing the plot ready for planting. Mark out the beds according to the plans you prepared earlier. You will need to separate these beds with paths to allow access to your plants. There are many ways to lay a path, some gardeners choose to lay down paving stones, others will place gravel over a sheet to stop the weeds growing through, or simply leave grass paths to walk along, though these can become problematic during the wet winter months. Raised beds are good for defining pathways, as there is usually some space between the wooden borders of each bed. Don't make the space between your paths too narrow as you will have to kneel down on them to tend to your crops and will also have to bring tools and push wheelbarrows along them.

If your plot has been left unattended for a while the ground will need to be prepared. Start by removing all the weeds. This can initially be done with a spade to clear densely covered areas, then remove the weed roots. Once you have cleared the area it is time to break up the soil and remove any rocks and stones.

Fertilizing is the next step. You can do this either by digging up the earth and adding organic matter or by spreading it on the soil and waiting for worms to mix the soil for you. The former is a guaranteed way to add nutrients to the soil but is labor intensive. The latter is the more natural option, produces excellent quality earth, and involves less work, but if you don't have many worms in the soil the process can take a long time. Be careful not to over-fertilize, as it can have adverse effects on plant development.

Crop rotation
Certain types of plants will take certain types of nutrients from the soil. If a plant is left in the same bed for too long, the supply of beneficial nutrients will be used up and the crop will fail. Crops also put nutrients into the soild which

Use a rake to flatten your plot and clear away any loose material that may get in the way of planting your crops.

will benefit other types of plants—this is where crop rotation comes in. By moving vegetables to a new patch every year, you are also protecting the plants from pests and diseases, which will become more prevalent if a crop is not moved. As a result you should see an improvement in the quality of yields as the quality of soil in the beds improves.

The most common form of crop rotation is the three group system, where one bed is allocated for root vegetables, one for legumes (beans, peas, lentils, etc), and one for brassicas (cabbages, broccoli, kale, etc). Some plants, particularly perennials like asparagus, can survive in the same place for an extended number of years, so don't worry about adding these crops to the list of beds that need rotating.

These raised beds allow easy access to all areas of the plot.

getting started

composting

The most important aspect of any gardening, and the key to real success, is to make sure that your soil is fertile, well balanced in essential nutrients, and moisture retentive without being too wet. Enthusiastic beginners often become downhearted at the poor progress of their plants, not realizing that an initial investment of time, thought, and research into soils and potting mixes will provide them with bounteous rewards.

Start your own compost pile

If you have enough outside space, the best thing to do is to start a compost pile or bin. There are many ready-made closed systems available, most of which consist of a large plastic bin with a close-fitting lid. Among the benefits of a compost pile or bin is a reduction in the amount of waste that needs to be collected from your home. Above all, you will have a rich compost full of beneficial organisms, including worms, to add to your purchased soil. You can buy worms to add to a composting bin. These will devour your vegetable waste and convert it into much sought-after wormcast, a particularly fine and fertile compost.

Making compost from household waste is a much more environmentally friendly way of giving plants nutrients than using chemical fertilizers.

What to put on the pile
The following will all make good compost:

- Vegetable peelings
- Vegetables and fruits way beyond their use-by date
- Dead flowers, along with the old flower water
- Fallen petals and leaves
- Corrugated cardboard
- Egg boxes
- Coffee grounds
- Tea leaves and tea bags
- Eggshells (never whole eggs)
- Grass clippings
- Weeds (but be careful not to include those in seed and bindweed)
- Torn-up newspaper
- Straw (essential)
- Fruit peelings

Feeding your plants

You can add well-rotted manure to a general-purpose potting mix to make a rich and nutritious medium in which to grow hungry plants, such as beans, peas, and zucchini (courgettes). It should not be used for root crops, such as carrots, however, since it will cause the roots to fork or distort. Spent mushroom compost, which contains a lot of straw, is wonderful for lightening the soil, but it is rich in lime, which doesn't suit all crops; strawberries and raspberries, for example, do not thrive in a lime-rich soil.

Crops grown in containers should ideally be fed a few weeks after planting to boost the fertility of the soil. There are many proprietary organic feeds available—some liquid and some that are incorporated into the surface of the soil. A weekly feed of seaweed extract or comfrey liquid is ideal. It is easy to make you own comfrey liquid, which is a great natural fertilizer. Simply fill an enamel bucket with comfrey leaves, place a heavy stone on top of them, add 1 pint (600ml) of water, and leave to rot in a warm place for a month. Next, drain the liquid from the bucket, this is the finished fertilizer. To use, make a solution of one part comfrey liquid to four parts water.

Borlotti beans with their wonderful coloring benefit from being planted in a nutritious potting mix.

Benefits of composting

- Compost enriches the soil by increasing the organic matter, so that plants are healthier and stronger.
- It provides natural, slow-release nutrients.
- Not only does compost help the soil to retain moisture; it also balances the pH levels.
- Compost reduces soil erosion.
- In winter, compost increases soil temperature, while in summer it lowers it, thus benefiting the plants.
- Sandy soils improve by gaining body, which will preserve moisture. Clay soils will gain a more open structure, so they drain better.

diseases and pests

The battle between gardeners and pests is never ending, but can be controlled. A great fuss is made about plant diseases and pests, much of it generated by chemical companies seeking to sell more products. Commercial preparations are usually best avoided, although there are a few benign chemicals that are allowed in the organic system. There is growing opposition to the use of chemicals in horticulture because of the environmental consequences.

In reality, the most effective way to combat disease or pests is to grow sturdy, healthy plants in a well-managed soil—these should survive occasional attacks from small pests if you are vigilant and react quickly. Don't overcrowd your plants, and allow good air circulation. Make sure they have enough light; sun is important, but don't let them overheat. Water regularly, and go easy on adding nutrients.

Insects

Although many insects, notably bees, are beneficial in the garden, a number of species can do significant damage to crops. Aphids are among the worst offenders. They attack a wide range of plants, including beets, peas, squash, and tomatoes. They damage plants by sucking the sap, causing leaves to twist or distort. The juicy bugs make nutritious food for fledgling birds; hover fly and ladybug larvae also rely on a healthy diet of aphids. If infestation is causing damage, a good blast of water from a hose will dislodge most of them.

The maggot of the root fly burrows deeply into carrots, while the flea beetle nips tiny holes in radishes, arugula (rocket), and brassicas. Fortunately, these two insects cannot fly above a height of about 8 inches (20cm), so can be deterred by erecting a low barrier around the plants.

Slugs and snails

Slugs and snails are greedy feeders, attracted by soft new growth, and they can demolish a plant overnight. They are a gardener's nemesis, but avoid using toxic pellets as they can

A traditional scarecrow is still a great deterrent for birds and other pests.

getting started

Using recycled material is a key part of modern gardening. Here empty water bottles have been modified to provide protection from slugs and snails.

Pots placed on top of sticks stop gardeners from wounding themselves on the points and also confuse birds and other creatures, thus protecting the emerging crop.

contaminate the soil and the poisoned snail and slug carcases may be eaten by toads or thrushes, with devastating consequences for those beneficial creatures. There is an organically approved pellet made from ferrous sulfate, which breaks down in the soil, but the best method of dealing with slugs and snails is to be vigilant and pick them off plants when you spot them. Slugs and snails feed at night, so a visit with a flashlight can result in quite a harvest. Put them in a bucket of salt water, which kills them quickly.

Another option is to place a mechanical barrier around a tender seedling—a plastic water bottle with the base cut away works well. An extra precaution is to wrap a strip of copper around the top of a pot; slugs and snails won't cross the metal. Scooped-out grapefruit shells placed skin up around your plants make handy hiding places for slugs and snails. Check them each day, and remove the culprits.

A sheet of fleece lining erected over crops will project them from birds and other airborne pests.

Cats and birds

Cats love fresh soil. Until your plants have grown, you could use a hard mulch, such as china shards or shells, to deter them. Birds may be a problem. In towns, pigeons can do a lot of damage; they love to peck at peas, chard, and cabbages. Blackbirds like berries of most kinds. Anything that flaps or whirrs—such as a child's pinwheel—will scare birds off.

Companion planting

Grow vegetables alongside other flowering plants if you can. The companion flowers will attract pollinating insects, which will also visit your bean and tomato flowers, your zucchini (courgettes), peppers, eggplants (aubergines), peas, and chilies. Chives or garlic alongside carrots will deter the root fly, and the aroma of basil or French marigolds growing near tomatoes will discourage white aphids. The herbs savory and thyme grown around fava (broad) beans will deter infestation of black aphids. Fennel and borage both invite bees and hover flies, the two most beneficial insects in the vegetable garden.

getting started

Weeding

Weeds can encourage disease in plants of the same species—for example, shepherd's purse and charlock are members of the brassica family. If they are harboring clubroot, this can be passed on to your cabbage crop.

Barriers

In many cases, a barrier will protect your plants adequately from pests. A floating row cover, made of porous polypropylene sheeting, will protect them from harmful insects. Fruit trees benefit from being covered with netting. If birds are denied the opportunity to feast on your fruits, they are more likely to eat slugs and flies.

More vigorous invaders require more substantial barriers. Rabbits may be put off by dense, thorny shrubs. For larger animals, a stout wire fence will be effective—or discourage them by planting species that they find repellent.

Try a few old cans suspended on strings; the flashing of the silver is a deterrent.

Protecting fruit trees

Tie corrugated cardboard around the trunks of fruit trees in late summer. It will provide a home for a variety of fruit-tree pests, such as moth grubs and weevils. Remove the cardboard after a week or two and destroy it; start again with new cardboard.

Crop rotation

To keep soil healthy, crop rotation is an essential part of organic gardening because each crop tends to leach the soil of a particular nutrient. Planting the same crop again and again will exhaust the soil of that nutrient. Crop rotation allows the nutrient balance to become re-established, and prevents pests and diseases particular to specific crops from building up in the soil. Never plant the same crop in the same bed for two years running. Use this journal to keep a record of your planting plans from year to year, because it is very easy to forget which plant has been grown in which bed.

By far the most useful and well tested companion plants are the fiery orange tagetes, with their pungent scent that deters whitefly and other aphids.

watering and mulching

Opposite: *Strawberries grow well during warmer months but make sure the plants are not left to dry out during hotter spells. A layer of straw mulch will protect the plant from excess heat.*

Vigilance about watering is vital when growing plants so you must maintain a careful balance—too much water and your plants will drown, too little and they will dry out. Various products are designed to aid water retention in compost; these are usually in the form of granules that swell and take up water. They must be used carefully because they alter a natural process and can lead to overwatering.

When to water?

It is preferable to check the soil regularly, looking for signs of thirst in your plants. Early morning or late in the evening are the best times to water. Plants can be damaged by watering in the hot sun; water droplets on a plant act like a lens, allowing the sun to burn the leaves. Too light a watering at the wrong time will encourage the roots to reach for the surface and risk scorching.

Slate is used as mulch for this container of salad plants. Take care when arranging the pieces not to damage or restrict young shoots.

Mulches

An effective way to counteract evaporation is to add a mulch around the base of the plants on the surface of the soil. Almost anything will do. Bark chips make a dark covering, whereas broken china or seashells are more decorative; comfrey leaves are nutritious as well as attractive. If you are growing strawberries, straw has the added advantage of lifting the berries off the soil and away from slugs.

Color and tone of mulches can be important—for example, the light tone of crushed seashells spread around the base of rainbow chard will reflect the light and speed up their growth.

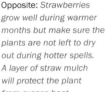

getting started

sowing and planting

Before you start planning your crops, you'll need to decide whether you're going to grow them from seed or if you're going to buy them as plug plants. Some seeds need to be nurtured under cover in seed trays or pots, while others can be planted directly outside and then the seedlings thinned out. It's therefore best to check the individual requirements for each plant type before deciding which ones to grow and in relation to how much space you have and the growing conditions available to you.

Growing from seed

Seeds need warmth, moisture, and soil to germinate. Some plants take longer than others to germinate depending on when you plant them and how warm it is. It's always best to sow more seeds than you need, as some may not germinate.

Some seeds will grow successfully outdoors in soil and a bit of fertilizer while others will require protection. If you have a polytunnel or cold frame, you can sow seeds under cover early so that the seedlings are ready to plant out once the soil is warm enough. If not, you can use a windowsill indoors. They can be sown in variety of different containers, such as small pots and cell trays. When using the latter, don't be tempted to put too many seeds in one cell, otherwise they will be fighting for root space and some may not thrive.

Transplanting seedlings

Some plants can be grown directly in their final growing space, particularly those that don't like their roots being disturbed, such as root crops, but many will benefit by being grown first in pots or in a seedbed and then being transplanted, especially if you are moving them from indoors to outdoors.

When seedlings have germinated and reached through the surface of the soil, make sure that they're big enough to handle before you transplant them or thin them out. A good

Top: *Newspaper pots can be planted directly into the soil and allowed to degrade naturally, thus avoiding any damage to tender young roots.*

Above: *These bean shoots are ready to be transported to their final outdoor growing space.*

An old fruit box is a useful container for young strawberry plants.

rule of thumb is to leave them until two or three leaves have grown, but some will need five or six. Follow the recommended instructions for each type of plant.

It's best to wait until all frosts have passed before planting most seedlings outdoors, and don't leave seedlings until the leaves have turned yellow or too big. Water the seedlings before transplanting or thinning to minimize shock and give them the best chance of recovery.

It's advisable to choose a dull day to transplant when the ground is moist. Make sure that the plants have been hardened off. To do this, put plants outside on mild days and bring them back in at night. Repeat for 10 days, then leave them outside for four nights to get them used to their new environment. Prepare the area where they will be planted by lightly forking up the soil and removing weeds. Rake in some well-rotted compost or add a base dressing of fertilizer.

When planting out make sure the soil of both the seedling and the new plot are moist to increase the chance of success.

Thinning

Seedlings usually need thinning out in order to give each one space to grow and thrive. If left as they are, the seedlings will have to fight for root space and nutrients in the compost and as a consequence will fail to grow properly, turn pale in color, and possibly die.

getting started

27

cuttings

So much money can be saved if you propagate your own plants by taking cuttings. It is very easy and most gratifying.

The best time to take cuttings is in spring or summer, when plants have new, vigorous, leafy growth. There are a variety of ways to propagate from cuttings, each with its own requirements. As a general rule, cuttings need adequate light, warmth, and moisture. Avoid taking very small cuttings because they tend to exhaust their food reserves before their roots are formed.

A free-draining rooting medium capable of retaining sufficient moisture will encourage the cuttings to form roots. Buy good-quality medium because using a sterilized medium prevents diseases from being passed on to vulnerable new plants.

Rosemary is one of the easiest plants to grow from cuttings.

Taking root

Some plants root easily if the cuttings are placed in water. Basil stems placed in a vase of water grow roots quickly, and the rooted cuttings can then be planted to create a good basil crop. Rooting hormone is very helpful when taking cuttings, because the organic compounds hasten the formation of roots, creating sturdier plants in a shorter time.

Woody-stemmed plants, such as lavender, box, and geraniums, are ideal sources of cuttings. All of these plants have the added benefit of creating a striking display when planted in quantity, such as box hedges surrounding beds.

Above: *Keep cuttings apart from each other in a seed tray, it makes them easier to plant out when they are ready to be handled.*

Opposite: *A container of box cuttings ready to prune and plant out to make a hedge. Simply cut a stem 4in (10cm) long, remove the bottom leaves, and put into any garden soil. After a year they will be well rooted.*

getting started

notes

notes

notes

Vegetables

There are five main vegetable groups: root vegetables, salad leaves, brassicas, legumes, and onions. There are also smaller groups that include pumpkins and tomatoes amongst others.

To successfully grow root vegetables, such as parsnips and radishes, the plants must have a steady source of nutrients in the soil, cool climate, and good drainage. Potatoes are a popular variety and achieve good yields in well-prepared soil, as will carrots and beetroot.

Salad leaves are quick and relatively simple to cultivate. They are shallow-rooting and need regular watering in the evenings to stop the compost drying out; prolonged drought stunts the growth of salad plants, producing tough bitter leaves.

Brassicas include cabbages and broccoli. They tend to flourish in cool, moist conditions and will suffer if exposed to a lot of direct sunlight. Plant brassicas in the same patch in late fall/autumn—most varieties grow in the same environment.

Legumes include beans of all kinds and are easy to grow. They suffer from few pests or diseases and tolerate most weather conditions. Another advantage is that they are highly nutritious—for some varieties it's best to eat the young green pods, while for others you can leave them on the plant to ripen into beans to be dried for eating in winter.

Plants from the onion family are a good choice for novices as they generally do not need much watering or nutrients. One thing onions do like is sunlight—plant them in a bright spot and weed regularly to avoid blocking out the sun.

root vegetables

Vegetable name

Variety planted

Seeds sown

Germination period

Seedlings planted out

Harvest

Successful varieties

Comments

Vegetable name

Variety planted

Seeds sown

Germination period

Seedlings planted out

Harvest

Successful varieties

Comments

Vegetable name

Variety planted

Seeds sown

Germination period

Seedlings planted out

Harvest

Successful varieties

Comments

Vegetable name

Variety planted

Seeds sown

Germination period

Seedlings planted out

Harvest

Successful varieties

Comments

Vegetable name

Variety planted

Seeds sown

Germination period

Seedlings planted out

Harvest

Successful varieties

Comments

Vegetable name

Variety planted

Seeds sown

Germination period

Seedlings planted out

Harvest

Successful varieties

Comments

Vegetable name

Variety planted

Seeds sown

Germination period

Seedlings planted out

Harvest

Successful varieties

Comments

Vegetable name

Variety planted

Seeds sown

Germination period

Seedlings planted out

Harvest

Successful varieties

Comments

root vegetables

Vegetable name

Variety planted

Seeds sown

Germination period

Seedlings planted out

Harvest

Successful varieties

Comments

Vegetable name

Variety planted

Seeds sown

Germination period

Seedlings planted out

Harvest

Successful varieties

Comments

Vegetable name

Variety planted

Seeds sown

Germination period

Seedlings planted out

Harvest

Successful varieties

Comments

Vegetable name

Variety planted

Seeds sown

Germination period

Seedlings planted out

Harvest

Successful varieties

Comments

vegetables

Vegetable name

Variety planted

Seeds sown

Germination period

Seedlings planted out

Harvest

Successful varieties

Comments

Vegetable name

Variety planted

Seeds sown

Germination period

Seedlings planted out

Harvest

Successful varieties

Comments

Vegetable name

Variety planted

Seeds sown

Germination period

Seedlings planted out

Harvest

Successful varieties

Comments

Vegetable name

Variety planted

Seeds sown

Germination period

Seedlings planted out

Harvest

Successful varieties

Comments

root vegetables

Vegetable name

Vegetable name

Variety planted

Variety planted

Seeds sown

Seeds sown

Germination period

Germination period

Seedlings planted out

Seedlings planted out

Harvest

Harvest

Successful varieties

Successful varieties

Comments

Comments

Vegetable name

Vegetable name

Variety planted

Variety planted

Seeds sown

Seeds sown

Germination period

Germination period

Seedlings planted out

Seedlings planted out

Harvest

Harvest

Successful varieties

Successful varieties

Comments

Comments

vegetables

Vegetable name

Variety planted

Seeds sown

Germination period

Seedlings planted out

Harvest

Successful varieties

Comments

Vegetable name

Variety planted

Seeds sown

Germination period

Seedlings planted out

Harvest

Successful varieties

Comments

Vegetable name

Variety planted

Seeds sown

Germination period

Seedlings planted out

Harvest

Successful varieties

Comments

Vegetable name

Variety planted

Seeds sown

Germination period

Seedlings planted out

Harvest

Successful varieties

Comments

vegetables

43

salad leaves

Vegetable name

Variety planted

Seeds sown

Germination period

Seedlings planted out

Harvest

Successful varieties

Comments

Vegetable name

Variety planted

Seeds sown

Germination period

Seedlings planted out

Harvest

Successful varieties

Comments

Vegetable name

Variety planted

Seeds sown

Germination period

Seedlings planted out

Harvest

Successful varieties

Comments

Vegetable name

Variety planted

Seeds sown

Germination period

Seedlings planted out

Harvest

Successful varieties

Comments

vegetables

44

Vegetable name

Variety planted

Seeds sown

Germination period

Seedlings planted out

Harvest

Successful varieties

Comments

Vegetable name

Variety planted

Seeds sown

Germination period

Seedlings planted out

Harvest

Successful varieties

Comments

Vegetable name

Variety planted

Seeds sown

Germination period

Seedlings planted out

Harvest

Successful varieties

Comments

Vegetable name

Variety planted

Seeds sown

Germination period

Seedlings planted out

Harvest

Successful varieties

Comments

salad leaves

Vegetable name

Variety planted

Seeds sown

Germination period

Seedlings planted out

Harvest

Successful varieties

Comments

Vegetable name

Variety planted

Seeds sown

Germination period

Seedlings planted out

Harvest

Successful varieties

Comments

Vegetable name

Variety planted

Seeds sown

Germination period

Seedlings planted out

Harvest

Successful varieties

Comments

Vegetable name

Variety planted

Seeds sown

Germination period

Seedlings planted out

Harvest

Successful varieties

Comments

Vegetable name

Variety planted

Seeds sown

Germination period

Seedlings planted out

Harvest

Successful varieties

Comments

Vegetable name

Variety planted

Seeds sown

Germination period

Seedlings planted out

Harvest

Successful varieties

Comments

Vegetable name

Variety planted

Seeds sown

Germination period

Seedlings planted out

Harvest

Successful varieties

Comments

Vegetable name

Variety planted

Seeds sown

Germination period

Seedlings planted out

Harvest

Successful varieties

Comments

vegetables

47

salad leaves

Vegetable name
_____

Variety planted
_____

Seeds sown
_____

Germination period
_____

Seedlings planted out
_____

Harvest
_____

Successful varieties
_____

Comments
_____
_____
_____
_____

Vegetable name
_____

Variety planted
_____

Seeds sown
_____

Germination period
_____

Seedlings planted out
_____

Harvest
_____

Successful varieties
_____

Comments
_____
_____
_____
_____

Vegetable name
_____

Variety planted
_____

Seeds sown
_____

Germination period
_____

Seedlings planted out
_____

Harvest
_____

Successful varieties
_____

Comments
_____
_____
_____
_____

Vegetable name
_____

Variety planted
_____

Seeds sown
_____

Germination period
_____

Seedlings planted out
_____

Harvest
_____

Successful varieties
_____

Comments
_____
_____
_____
_____

vegetables

Vegetable name

Variety planted

Seeds sown

Germination period

Seedlings planted out

Harvest

Successful varieties

Comments

Vegetable name

Variety planted

Seeds sown

Germination period

Seedlings planted out

Harvest

Successful varieties

Comments

Vegetable name

Variety planted

Seeds sown

Germination period

Seedlings planted out

Harvest

Successful varieties

Comments

Vegetable name

Variety planted

Seeds sown

Germination period

Seedlings planted out

Harvest

Successful varieties

Comments

vegetables

brassicas

Vegetable name

Variety planted

Seeds sown

Germination period

Seedlings planted out

Harvest

Successful varieties

Comments

Vegetable name

Variety planted

Seeds sown

Germination period

Seedlings planted out

Harvest

Successful varieties

Comments

Vegetable name

Variety planted

Seeds sown

Germination period

Seedlings planted out

Harvest

Successful varieties

Comments

Vegetable name

Variety planted

Seeds sown

Germination period

Seedlings planted out

Harvest

Successful varieties

Comments

Vegetable name

Variety planted

Seeds sown

Germination period

Seedlings planted out

Harvest

Successful varieties

Comments

Vegetable name

Variety planted

Seeds sown

Germination period

Seedlings planted out

Harvest

Successful varieties

Comments

Vegetable name

Variety planted

Seeds sown

Germination period

Seedlings planted out

Harvest

Successful varieties

Comments

Vegetable name

Variety planted

Seeds sown

Germination period

Seedlings planted out

Harvest

Successful varieties

Comments

vegetables

brassicas

Vegetable name

Variety planted

Seeds sown

Germination period

Seedlings planted out

Harvest

Successful varieties

Comments

Vegetable name

Variety planted

Seeds sown

Germination period

Seedlings planted out

Harvest

Successful varieties

Comments

Vegetable name

Variety planted

Seeds sown

Germination period

Seedlings planted out

Harvest

Successful varieties

Comments

Vegetable name

Variety planted

Seeds sown

Germination period

Seedlings planted out

Harvest

Successful varieties

Comments

vegetables

Vegetable name

Variety planted

Seeds sown

Germination period

Seedlings planted out

Harvest

Successful varieties

Comments

Vegetable name

Variety planted

Seeds sown

Germination period

Seedlings planted out

Harvest

Successful varieties

Comments

Vegetable name

Variety planted

Seeds sown

Germination period

Seedlings planted out

Harvest

Successful varieties

Comments

Vegetable name

Variety planted

Seeds sown

Germination period

Seedlings planted out

Harvest

Successful varieties

Comments

vegetables

53

brassicas

Vegetable name

Variety planted

Seeds sown

Germination period

Seedlings planted out

Harvest

Successful varieties

Comments

Vegetable name

Variety planted

Seeds sown

Germination period

Seedlings planted out

Harvest

Successful varieties

Comments

Vegetable name

Variety planted

Seeds sown

Germination period

Seedlings planted out

Harvest

Successful varieties

Comments

Vegetable name

Variety planted

Seeds sown

Germination period

Seedlings planted out

Harvest

Successful varieties

Comments

vegetables

Vegetable name

Variety planted

Seeds sown

Germination period

Seedlings planted out

Harvest

Successful varieties

Comments

Vegetable name

Variety planted

Seeds sown

Germination period

Seedlings planted out

Harvest

Successful varieties

Comments

Vegetable name

Variety planted

Seeds sown

Germination period

Seedlings planted out

Harvest

Successful varieties

Comments

Vegetable name

Variety planted

Seeds sown

Germination period

Seedlings planted out

Harvest

Successful varieties

Comments

vegetables

legumes

Vegetable name

Variety planted

Seeds sown

Germination period

Seedlings planted out

Harvest

Successful varieties

Comments

Vegetable name

Variety planted

Seeds sown

Germination period

Seedlings planted out

Harvest

Successful varieties

Comments

Vegetable name

Variety planted

Seeds sown

Germination period

Seedlings planted out

Harvest

Successful varieties

Comments

Vegetable name

Variety planted

Seeds sown

Germination period

Seedlings planted out

Harvest

Successful varieties

Comments

Vegetable name

Variety planted

Seeds sown

Germination period

Seedlings planted out

Harvest

Successful varieties

Comments

Vegetable name

Variety planted

Seeds sown

Germination period

Seedlings planted out

Harvest

Successful varieties

Comments

Vegetable name

Variety planted

Seeds sown

Germination period

Seedlings planted out

Harvest

Successful varieties

Comments

Vegetable name

Variety planted

Seeds sown

Germination period

Seedlings planted out

Harvest

Successful varieties

Comments

legumes

Vegetable name

Variety planted

Seeds sown

Germination period

Seedlings planted out

Harvest

Successful varieties

Comments

Vegetable name

Variety planted

Seeds sown

Germination period

Seedlings planted out

Harvest

Successful varieties

Comments

Vegetable name

Variety planted

Seeds sown

Germination period

Seedlings planted out

Harvest

Successful varieties

Comments

Vegetable name

Variety planted

Seeds sown

Germination period

Seedlings planted out

Harvest

Successful varieties

Comments

Vegetable name

Variety planted

Seeds sown

Germination period

Seedlings planted out

Harvest

Successful varieties

Comments

Vegetable name

Variety planted

Seeds sown

Germination period

Seedlings planted out

Harvest

Successful varieties

Comments

Vegetable name

Variety planted

Seeds sown

Germination period

Seedlings planted out

Harvest

Successful varieties

Comments

Vegetable name

Variety planted

Seeds sown

Germination period

Seedlings planted out

Harvest

Successful varieties

Comments

onions

Vegetable name

Variety planted

Seeds sown

Germination period

Seedlings planted out

Harvest

Successful varieties

Comments

Vegetable name

Variety planted

Seeds sown

Germination period

Seedlings planted out

Harvest

Successful varieties

Comments

Vegetable name

Variety planted

Seeds sown

Germination period

Seedlings planted out

Harvest

Successful varieties

Comments

Vegetable name

Variety planted

Seeds sown

Germination period

Seedlings planted out

Harvest

Successful varieties

Comments

Vegetable name

Variety planted

Seeds sown

Germination period

Seedlings planted out

Harvest

Successful varieties

Comments

Vegetable name

Variety planted

Seeds sown

Germination period

Seedlings planted out

Harvest

Successful varieties

Comments

Vegetable name

Variety planted

Seeds sown

Germination period

Seedlings planted out

Harvest

Successful varieties

Comments

Vegetable name

Variety planted

Seeds sown

Germination period

Seedlings planted out

Harvest

Successful varieties

Comments

vegetables

onions

Vegetable name

Vegetable name

Variety planted

Variety planted

Seeds sown

Seeds sown

Germination period

Germination period

Seedlings planted out

Seedlings planted out

Harvest

Harvest

Successful varieties

Successful varieties

Comments

Comments

Vegetable name

Vegetable name

Variety planted

Variety planted

Seeds sown

Seeds sown

Germination period

Germination period

Seedlings planted out

Seedlings planted out

Harvest

Harvest

Successful varieties

Successful varieties

Comments

Comments

Vegetable name

Variety planted

Seeds sown

Germination period

Seedlings planted out

Harvest

Successful varieties

Comments

Vegetable name

Variety planted

Seeds sown

Germination period

Seedlings planted out

Harvest

Successful varieties

Comments

Vegetable name

Variety planted

Seeds sown

Germination period

Seedlings planted out

Harvest

Successful varieties

Comments

Vegetable name

Variety planted

Seeds sown

Germination period

Seedlings planted out

Harvest

Successful varieties

Comments

vegetables

63

tomatoes

Vegetable name

Variety planted

Seeds sown

Germination period

Seedlings planted out

Harvest

Successful varieties

Comments

Vegetable name

Variety planted

Seeds sown

Germination period

Seedlings planted out

Harvest

Successful varieties

Comments

Vegetable name

Variety planted

Seeds sown

Germination period

Seedlings planted out

Harvest

Successful varieties

Comments

Vegetable name

Variety planted

Seeds sown

Germination period

Seedlings planted out

Harvest

Successful varieties

Comments

Vegetable name

Variety planted

Seeds sown

Germination period

Seedlings planted out

Harvest

Successful varieties

Comments

Vegetable name

Variety planted

Seeds sown

Germination period

Seedlings planted out

Harvest

Successful varieties

Comments

Vegetable name

Variety planted

Seeds sown

Germination period

Seedlings planted out

Harvest

Successful varieties

Comments

Vegetable name

Variety planted

Seeds sown

Germination period

Seedlings planted out

Harvest

Successful varieties

Comments

vegetables

65

tomatoes

Vegetable name
....

Vegetable name
....

Variety planted
....

Variety planted
....

Seeds sown
....

Seeds sown
....

Germination period
....

Germination period
....

Seedlings planted out
....

Seedlings planted out
....

Harvest
....

Harvest
....

Successful varieties
....

Successful varieties
....

Comments
....
....
....
....

Comments
....
....
....
....

Vegetable name
....

Vegetable name
....

Variety planted
....

Variety planted
....

Seeds sown
....

Seeds sown
....

Germination period
....

Germination period
....

Seedlings planted out
....

Seedlings planted out
....

Harvest
....

Harvest
....

Successful varieties
....

Successful varieties
....

Comments
....
....
....
....

Comments
....
....
....
....

vegetables

Vegetable name

Variety planted

Seeds sown

Germination period

Seedlings planted out

Harvest

Successful varieties

Comments

Vegetable name

Variety planted

Seeds sown

Germination period

Seedlings planted out

Harvest

Successful varieties

Comments

Vegetable name

Variety planted

Seeds sown

Germination period

Seedlings planted out

Harvest

Successful varieties

Comments

Vegetable name

Variety planted

Seeds sown

Germination period

Seedlings planted out

Harvest

Successful varieties

Comments

vegetables

67

other vegetables

Vegetable name

Variety planted

Seeds sown

Germination period

Seedlings planted out

Harvest

Successful varieties

Comments

Vegetable name

Variety planted

Seeds sown

Germination period

Seedlings planted out

Harvest

Successful varieties

Comments

Vegetable name

Variety planted

Seeds sown

Germination period

Seedlings planted out

Harvest

Successful varieties

Comments

Vegetable name

Variety planted

Seeds sown

Germination period

Seedlings planted out

Harvest

Successful varieties

Comments

Vegetable name

Variety planted

Seeds sown

Germination period

Seedlings planted out

Harvest

Successful varieties

Comments

Vegetable name

Variety planted

Seeds sown

Germination period

Seedlings planted out

Harvest

Successful varieties

Comments

Vegetable name

Variety planted

Seeds sown

Germination period

Seedlings planted out

Harvest

Successful varieties

Comments

Vegetable name

Variety planted

Seeds sown

Germination period

Seedlings planted out

Harvest

Successful varieties

Comments

vegetables

other vegetables

Vegetable name

Variety planted

Seeds sown

Germination period

Seedlings planted out

Harvest

Successful varieties

Comments

Vegetable name

Variety planted

Seeds sown

Germination period

Seedlings planted out

Harvest

Successful varieties

Comments

Vegetable name

Variety planted

Seeds sown

Germination period

Seedlings planted out

Harvest

Successful varieties

Comments

Vegetable name

Variety planted

Seeds sown

Germination period

Seedlings planted out

Harvest

Successful varieties

Comments

Vegetable name

Variety planted

Seeds sown

Germination period

Seedlings planted out

Harvest

Successful varieties

Comments

Vegetable name

Variety planted

Seeds sown

Germination period

Seedlings planted out

Harvest

Successful varieties

Comments

Vegetable name

Variety planted

Seeds sown

Germination period

Seedlings planted out

Harvest

Successful varieties

Comments

Vegetable name

Variety planted

Seeds sown

Germination period

Seedlings planted out

Harvest

Successful varieties

Comments

notes

vegetables

notes

notes

notes

Fruit

Even if you have only a small outdoor space, you can still grow some of your own fruit, either on a tree or in plant form. Many fruit-bearing plants grow happily in containers, and some orchard trees have been bred especially for this purpose. As a rule fruits suffer in cold conditions, so protect plants carefully from frost and winds and make sure they are in a position where they receive a decent amount of sunlight.

Grape vines thrive if grown in a warm, sunny place. They need enough soil to retain moisture, and should be pruned regularly to reduce leafy growth and promote a well-formed plant that will yield a fair harvest. A good nursery will advise on the best type of vine for your climate and conditions.

Strawberries are one of the easiest fruits to grow. Both cultivated strawberries and the wild or alpine type need to be kept moist and will tolerate some shade. Allow the berries to ripen fully to a dark red color, and pick them to eat straight from the plant.

Physalis (also called cape gooseberries) are easy to grow and generally not attacked by pests. Seeds germinate quickly, or you can buy young plants. Like tomatoes, to which they are closely related, physalis need warmth and sun to ripen.

All fruit will benefit from a weekly high-potash liquid feed when the fruit begins to mature. A tomato feed is ideal; organic varieties are readily available.

tree fruit

Fruit name

Variety planted

Harvest

Successful varieties

Comments

Fruit name

Variety planted

Harvest

Successful varieties

Comments

Fruit name

Variety planted

Harvest

Successful varieties

Comments

Fruit name

Variety planted

Harvest

Successful varieties

Comments

Fruit name

Variety planted

Harvest
Successful varieties

Comments

Fruit name

Variety planted

Harvest
Successful varieties

Comments

Fruit name

Variety planted

Harvest
Successful varieties

Comments

Fruit name

Variety planted

Harvest
Successful varieties

Comments

fruit

tree fruit

Fruit name

Variety planted

Harvest

Successful varieties

Comments

Fruit name

Variety planted

Harvest

Successful varieties

Comments

Fruit name

Variety planted

Harvest

Successful varieties

Comments

Fruit name

Variety planted

Harvest

Successful varieties

Comments

Fruit name

Variety planted

Harvest

Successful varieties

Comments

Fruit name

Variety planted

Harvest

Successful varieties

Comments

Fruit name

Variety planted

Harvest

Successful varieties

Comments

Fruit name

Variety planted

Harvest

Successful varieties

Comments

fruit

tree fruit

Fruit name

Variety planted

Harvest
Successful varieties

Comments

Fruit name

Variety planted

Harvest
Successful varieties

Comments

Fruit name

Variety planted

Harvest
Successful varieties

Comments

Fruit name

Variety planted

Harvest
Successful varieties

Comments

Fruit name

Variety planted

Harvest
Successful varieties

Comments

Fruit name

Variety planted

Harvest
Successful varieties

Comments

Fruit name

Variety planted

Harvest
Successful varieties

Comments

Fruit name

Variety planted

Harvest
Successful varieties

Comments

bush fruit

Fruit name

Variety planted

Harvest

Successful varieties

Comments

Fruit name

Variety planted

Harvest

Successful varieties

Comments

Fruit name

Variety planted

Harvest

Successful varieties

Comments

Fruit name

Variety planted

Harvest

Successful varieties

Comments

fruit

Fruit name

Variety planted

Harvest
Successful varieties

Comments

Fruit name

Variety planted

Harvest
Successful varieties

Comments

Fruit name

Variety planted

Harvest
Successful varieties

Comments

Fruit name

Variety planted

Harvest
Successful varieties

Comments

bush fruit

Fruit name

Variety planted

Harvest

Successful varieties

Comments

Fruit name

Variety planted

Harvest

Successful varieties

Comments

Fruit name

Variety planted

Harvest

Successful varieties

Comments

Fruit name

Variety planted

Harvest

Successful varieties

Comments

Fruit name

Variety planted

Harvest
Successful varieties

Comments

Fruit name

Variety planted

Harvest
Successful varieties

Comments

Fruit name

Variety planted

Harvest
Successful varieties

Comments

Fruit name

Variety planted

Harvest
Successful varieties

Comments

fruit

bush fruit

Fruit name

Variety planted

Harvest
Successful varieties

Comments

Fruit name

Variety planted

Harvest
Successful varieties

Comments

Fruit name

Variety planted

Harvest
Successful varieties

Comments

Fruit name

Variety planted

Harvest
Successful varieties

Comments

Fruit name

Variety planted

Harvest
Successful varieties

Comments

Fruit name

Variety planted

Harvest
Successful varieties

Comments

Fruit name

Variety planted

Harvest
Successful varieties

Comments

Fruit name

Variety planted

Harvest
Successful varieties

Comments

notes

fruit

notes

fruit

notes

fruit

Herbs

As long as herbs have good soil, plenty of light, and a fair amount of sun and warmth, most herbs will thrive. If you are new to vegetable gardening, it is no bad thing to start by growing herbs. You will soon graduate to growing vegetables, and then you can put your herbs and vegetables together in the kitchen and create some delicious meals.

Among hardy perennial herbs that can survive at quite low temperatures are the alliums. This family includes chives, a useful everyday herb that is easy to grow and has pretty purple, edible flowers. Welsh onions are similar to chives but have rather bulbous hollow leaves; and garlic chives have straplike leaves and lovely white flowers.

Sweet majoram, oregano, and thyme will tolerate dry conditions. Tarragon needs space, but is also worth growing—make sure you choose the French type, it has the best flavor. Rosemary and sage are larger evergreen shrubs with a woody framework and should be planted with a good depth of potting mix. Mint is also popular with gardeners—Korean and American mountain mints are good for making tea.

Annual herbs, which last for one season only, should be grown from seed. Indispensable varieties include basil, dill, and cilantro (coriander). Garden chervil is another annual herb, and is useful for cooking. Annuals will flower and set seed in a season.

herbs

Herb name

Variety planted

Seeds sown

Germination period

Seedlings planted out

Harvest

Successful varieties

Comments

Herb name

Variety planted

Seeds sown

Germination period

Seedlings planted out

Harvest

Successful varieties

Comments

Herb name

Variety planted

Seeds sown

Germination period

Seedlings planted out

Harvest

Successful varieties

Comments

Herb name

Variety planted

Seeds sown

Germination period

Seedlings planted out

Harvest

Successful varieties

Comments

Herb name

Variety planted

Seeds sown

Germination period

Seedlings planted out

Harvest

Successful varieties

Comments

Herb name

Variety planted

Seeds sown

Germination period

Seedlings planted out

Harvest

Successful varieties

Comments

Herb name

Variety planted

Seeds sown

Germination period

Seedlings planted out

Harvest

Successful varieties

Comments

Herb name

Variety planted

Seeds sown

Germination period

Seedlings planted out

Harvest

Successful varieties

Comments

herbs

herbs

Herb name

Variety planted

Seeds sown

Germination period

Seedlings planted out

Harvest

Successful varieties

Comments

Herb name

Variety planted

Seeds sown

Germination period

Seedlings planted out

Harvest

Successful varieties

Comments

Herb name

Variety planted

Seeds sown

Germination period

Seedlings planted out

Harvest

Successful varieties

Comments

Herb name

Variety planted

Seeds sown

Germination period

Seedlings planted out

Harvest

Successful varieties

Comments

Herb name

Variety planted

Seeds sown

Germination period

Seedlings planted out

Harvest

Successful varieties

Comments

Herb name

Variety planted

Seeds sown

Germination period

Seedlings planted out

Harvest

Successful varieties

Comments

Herb name

Variety planted

Seeds sown

Germination period

Seedlings planted out

Harvest

Successful varieties

Comments

Herb name

Variety planted

Seeds sown

Germination period

Seedlings planted out

Harvest

Successful varieties

Comments

herbs

herbs

Herb name

Variety planted

Seeds sown

Germination period

Seedlings planted out

Harvest

Successful varieties

Comments

Herb name

Variety planted

Seeds sown

Germination period

Seedlings planted out

Harvest

Successful varieties

Comments

Herb name

Variety planted

Seeds sown

Germination period

Seedlings planted out

Harvest

Successful varieties

Comments

Herb name

Variety planted

Seeds sown

Germination period

Seedlings planted out

Harvest

Successful varieties

Comments

herbs

106

Herb name

Variety planted

Seeds sown

Germination period

Seedlings planted out

Harvest

Successful varieties

Comments

Herb name

Variety planted

Seeds sown

Germination period

Seedlings planted out

Harvest

Successful varieties

Comments

Herb name

Variety planted

Seeds sown

Germination period

Seedlings planted out

Harvest

Successful varieties

Comments

Herb name

Variety planted

Seeds sown

Germination period

Seedlings planted out

Harvest

Successful varieties

Comments

herbs

Herb name

Variety planted

Seeds sown

Germination period

Seedlings planted out

Harvest

Successful varieties

Comments

Herb name

Variety planted

Seeds sown

Germination period

Seedlings planted out

Harvest

Successful varieties

Comments

Herb name

Variety planted

Seeds sown

Germination period

Seedlings planted out

Harvest

Successful varieties

Comments

Herb name

Variety planted

Seeds sown

Germination period

Seedlings planted out

Harvest

Successful varieties

Comments

Herb name

Variety planted

Seeds sown

Germination period

Seedlings planted out

Harvest

Successful varieties

Comments

Herb name

Variety planted

Seeds sown

Germination period

Seedlings planted out

Harvest

Successful varieties

Comments

Herb name

Variety planted

Seeds sown

Germination period

Seedlings planted out

Harvest

Successful varieties

Comments

Herb name

Variety planted

Seeds sown

Germination period

Seedlings planted out

Harvest

Successful varieties

Comments

notes

herbs

herbs

year planner

January	
February	
March	
April	
May	
June	
July	
August	
September	
October	
November	
December	

January	
February	
March	
April	
May	
June	
July	
August	
September	
October	
November	
December	

year planner

year planner

January	
February	
March	
April	
May	
June	
July	
August	
September	
October	
November	
December	

January	
February	
March	
April	
May	
June	
July	
August	
September	
October	
November	
December	

year planner

year planner

January	
February	
March	
April	
May	
June	
July	
August	
September	
October	
November	
December	

January	
February	
March	
April	
May	
June	
July	
August	
September	
October	
November	
December	

useful contacts

US

Backyardgardener, LLC
backyardgardener.com
Info site for organic
gardening.

Biodelice
biodelice.com
Organic food and sustainable
agriculture.

City Gardening magazine
Magazine written for
gardeners who grow fruits,
herbs, and veg in a city.
Subscribe at
citygardeningmagazine.com

Composters.com
Tel: 1 877 20 GREEN
composters.com
Information on potting mixes.

GardenMandy
gardenmandy.com
Organic gardening online
tips.

LandscapeUSA
Tel: 800 966 1033
landscapeusa.com

T&J Enterprises
Tel: 1 800 998 8692
Outside the USA:
1 509 327 7670
tandjenterprises.com
Organic gardening products.

gardenplantcare.com
Good gardening tips and
seeds.

gardensimply.com
Monthly tips on sustainable
organic gardening practice.

gardening-advice.org
Gardening tips and advice.

organicgardening.com
Organic Gardening magazine.

the-organic-gardener.com
Explains organic gardening,
how to use gardening tools
effectively, organic weed
control, compost gardening
and more.

thegardenersresource.com
General gardening advice,
including info on growing
herbs.

pennystomatoes.com
Tomato seeds and recipes.

SEED SUPPLIERS

**Eden Organic Nursery
Services**
Tel: 954 382 8281
eonseed.com

Heirloom Seeds
Tel: 412 384 0852
heirloomseeds.com

Johnny's Selected Seeds
Toll Free: 1 877 564 6697
johnnyseeds.com

**Marianna's Heirloom
Tomatoes**
Tel: 615 446 9191
mariseeds.com

Neseed.com
3580 Main Street,
Hartford CT 06120
Toll free phone:
800 825 5477

organiccatalog.com
Organic seeds.

Park Seed Company
Orders: info@parkscs.com
For gardening advice:
gardener@parkscs.com
parkseed.com

Richters Herbs
Tel: +1 905 640 6677
richters.com

Seeds from Italy
Tel: 781 721 5904
growitalian.com

Seeds of Change
seedsofchange.com
Store-finder: 1 888 762 4240

Territorial Seed Company
Phone Orders:
800 626 0866
Customer service/gardening
questions: 541 942 9547
info@territorialseed.com

Victory Seed Company
Tel: (503) 829-3126
info@victoryseeds.com
victoryseeds.com

UK

Allotment Growing
allotment.org.uk
Useful advice on all aspects
of allotment gardening.

BBC Gardening
bbc.co.uk/gardening
Advice on all aspects of
gardening.

**Garden Organic
(previously HDRA)**
Tel: 02476 303517
gardenorganic.org.uk
Offers advice and
information about organic
gardening.

Green Gardener
Tel: 01603 715096
greengardener.co.uk
Specialists in effective
organic pest controls

Let's Go Gardening
letsgogardening.co.uk
General gardening
information.

Rocket Gardens
Tel: 01209 831468
rocketgardens.co.uk
Distributer of organic
seedlings.

Royal Horticultural Society
Tel: 0845 260 5000
Gardening advice for RHS
members: 0845 260 8000
rhs.org.uk
Provides advice and a
gardener's calendar.

The Herb Society
Tel: 0845 491 8699
herbsociety.co.uk

National Vegetable Society
nvsuk.org.uk
Various articles on growing
vegetables, fruit, and herbs.

The Organic Gardener
the-organic-gardener.com
Explains organic gardening,
how to use tools, organic
weed control, composting,
and more.

The Soil Association
Tel: 0117 314 5000
soilassociation.org
The UK's leading
environmental charity
promoting sustainable,
organic farming.
See also: whyorganic.org

Town and City Gardens
gardening-centre.co.uk
Information and online shop.

Vegetable Garden
vegetable-gardens.co.uk
Vegetable growing guides and
a forum to ask for advice.

Vegetable Plants Direct
Tel: 01288 321175
vegetableplantsdirect.co.uk
Company selling organically
grown and non-organic plants.

SEED SUPPLIERS

Association Kokopelli
terredesemences.com
Lists 1,000 varieties of
organic seeds available to buy
online.

Beans and Herbs
beansandherbs.co.uk

Chiltern Seeds
chilternseeds.co.uk

Dobies of Devon
Tel: 0844 701 7623
dobies.co.uk

D.T. Brown
Tel: 0845 371 0532
dtbrownseeds.co.uk

Garden Seeds UK
Tel: 01243 829584
gardenseeds.co.uk

Harrod Horticultural
Tel: 0845 218 5301
harrodhorticultural.com
Equipment and organic
seeds.

MAS Seed Specialists
Tel: 01249 819013
meadowmania.co.uk

Mr Fothergill's
Tel: 0845 371 0518
mr-fothergills.co.uk

Nicky's Nursery
Tel: 01843 600972
nickys-nursery.co.uk

Suttons
Tel: 0844 922 0606
suttons.co.uk

**The Organic Gardening
Catalogue**
Tel: 0845 130 1304
organiccatalog.com
The official catalogue of
Garden Organic (HDRA).

The Real Seed Catalogue
Tel: 01239 821107
realseeds.co.uk

Seeds of Italy
Tel: 020 8427 5020
seedsofitaly.com

Suffolk Herbs
Tel: 01376 572456
suffolkherbs.com

Thompson & Morgan
Tel: 0844 2485383
thompson-morgan.com

Tuckers Seeds
Tel: 01364 652233
tuckers-seeds.co.uk

Unwins
Tel: 01480 443395
unwins.co.uk

useful contacts

123

favorite gardening stores

Name

Address

Tel

Email www.

Comments

Name

Address

Tel

Email www.

Comments

Name

Address

Tel

Email www.

Comments

Name

Address

Tel

Email www.

Comments

Name

Address

Tel

Email www.

Comments

Name

Address

Tel

Email www.

Comments

Name

Address

Tel

Email www.

Comments

Name

Address

Tel

Email www.

Comments

favorite gardening websites

www.

Notes

www.

Notes

www.

Notes

www.

Notes

www.

Notes

www.

Notes

www.

Notes

www.

Notes

www.

Notes

www.

Notes

www. ....

Notes ....

....

....

....

www. ....

Notes ....

....

....

....

www. ....

Notes ....

....

....

....

www. ....

Notes ....

....

....

....

www. ....

Notes ....

....

....

....

www. ....

Notes ....

....

....

....

www. ....

Notes ....

....

....

....

www. ....

Notes ....

....

....

....

www. ....

Notes ....

....

....

....

www. ....

Notes ....

....

....

....

picture credits

Key: a=above, b=below, r=right, l=left

Jonathan Buckley
5a, 17

Roger Hammond
22, 28b, 29

Caroline Hughes
2, 10a, 14, 15, 16, 19b, 27b, 37a

David Mereweather
1, 37b, 101a

Heini Schneebeli
10b, 12, 19a, 23b, 24, 26a and b,
27a, 28a, 81a and b

Lucinda Symons
10bl, 18, 21, 25

Pia Tryde
5b, 23a, 101b

Polly Wreford
20

Francesca Yorke
13, 21l

Published in 2010 by CICO Books
An imprint of Ryland Peters & Small Ltd
20–21 Jockey's Fields   519 Broadway, 5th Floor
London WC1R 4BW   New York, NY 10012

www.cicobooks.com

10 9 8 7 6 5 4 3 2

Text © Tessa Evelegh, Deborah Schneebeli-Morrell,
Christina Strutt, and Nicki Trench 2010
Design and photography © CICO Books 2010

A CIP catalog record for this book is available from
the Library of Congress and the British Library.

US ISBN-13: 978 1 907030 29 1

UK ISBN-13: 978 1 907030 28 4

Printed in China

Editor: Pete Jorgensen
Designer: Roger Hammond,
bluegumdesigners.com